The Wellness Wheel _____ 2

The "Reclaiming the Joy of Ministry" Workbook Series _____ 3

Using the Vocational Wellness Workbook _____ 6

"Reclaiming the Joy of Ministry": Vocational Wellness _____ 8

Step One
Understanding Vocational Wellness _____ 9
Prayer for the Journey   9
Selecting Priority Activities   9
A. Vocational Wellness in One Word: Humility   10
Biblical reflections on Humility   11
B. The Heart of the Issue   13
C. Reflection on the Marker   14
D. Lesson Nine Assessments   15
E. Scripture Study on Vocational Wellness   15
F. Jesus and Vocational Wellness   19
G. The Fruit of the Spirit Is Gentleness   19
Bible Study on Gentleness   19
H. The Joy of Gentleness: How Joy Flows from This Fruit   21
I. Hymn/Song that Expresses the Joy of Vocational Gentleness   22
J. Summary Conclusion of Step One: Humility and Gentleness in Ministry   23

Step Two
Understanding Vocational Brokenness 24
Prayer for the Journey   24
Selecting Priority Activities   24
A. Review "Reclaiming the Joy"   25
B. Self-Assessment   25
C. Healthy/Unhealthy Scale   26
D. #1 Indicator of Vocational Brokenness: Diminished Joy   26
E. #2 Indicator of Vocational Brokenness: Leaving the Ministry   28
F. Identifying the Causes of Vocational Brokenness 29
G. Naming My Vocational Struggle   31
H. Self-Awareness   32
I. Biblical Examples   33
J. Personal Examples   33
K. Summary Conclusion of Step Two: How Am I Experiencing Vocational Brokenness?   33
L. Join The Grace Place Wellness Community   34

Step Three
Understanding Vocational Healing _____ 35
Prayer for the Journey   35
Selecting Priority Activities   35
A. Ephesians 4:11-12   36
B. Past History of Vocational Wellness   39
C. Hope for the Future: "Healing could be like…"   40
D. Substantial Healing: The Devotional Model from "Sculptor Spirit"   41

Gospel Resources for
E. Personal Reading Lis[t]
F. Suggested Reading
G. Confessional Statem[ent]
H. Liturgical and Musica[l Resources]
I. Institutional Resources   43
J. People Resources   44
K. Vision Statement: My Desired Future Condition   44
L. Join The Grace Place Wellness Community   46
M. Summary Conclusion of Step Three: My Vision for Vocational Wholeness   46
Before Proceeding to Step Four…   47
The Readiness for Change Index   47
Should I Complete Step Four?   48

Step Four
Welcoming the Healing Spirit _____ 49
Prayer for the Journey   49
Selecting Priority Activities   49
Drafting a Goal Statement   50
A. Review of the Process So Far   50
B. Beginning to Put the Past Behind   51
C. Advice to Self   52
D. Ideas for Welcoming the Healing Spirit   53
E. Goals that REACH   55
F. Developing an Action Plan   56
G. Institutional Resources   57
H. People Resources   58
I. Accountability and Encouragement   58
J. Prayer Journaling   59
K. Periodic Assessment of My Wellness Journey   59
L. Celebration of the Lord's Healing Work   60
M. Next REACH Goals for Continued Healing   60
N. Summary Conclusion of Step Four   61

Step Five
Welcoming the Spirit of Joy _____ 62
Prayer for the Journey   62
Selecting Priority Activities   62
Drafting a Goal Statement   62
A. Review of the Process So Far   62
B. Looking to the Future   64
C. Advice to Self   65
D. Ideas for Welcoming the Spirit of Joy   66
E. Goals that REACH   68
F. Developing an Action Plan   69
G. Institutional Resources   70
H. People Resources   71
I. Accountability and Encouragement   71
J. Prayer Journaling   72
K. Periodic Assessment of My Wellness Journey   73
L. Celebration of the Lord's Sustaining Work   74
M. Summary Conclusion of Step Five   74

Final Words of Encouragement _____ 76
Grace Along the Way   76
Our Prayer for You   76

The Wellness Wheel

RELATIONAL WELLBEING

SPIRITUAL WELLBEING

INTELLECTUAL WELLBEING

EMOTIONAL WELLBEING

In baptism — a new creation in Christ

VOCATIONAL WELLBEING

PHYSICAL WELLBEING

FINANCIAL WELLBEING

SPIRITUAL WELLBEING

Our Guide for the Workbook Series

The Wellness Wheel was first suggested as an assessment tool for professional church workers and the congregations they serve in 1997. Grace Place Wellness Ministries has shared the Wheel with thousands of workers and hundreds of congregations because it so beautifully expresses the inter-related nature of all the aspects of wellbeing. We experience God's Shalom of wholeness and unity only to the degree that we find Christ's healing grace at work in all aspects of life: Baptismal, Spiritual, Relational, Intellectual, Emotional, Vocational, Physical and Financial.

Baptismal and Spiritual Wellness, the center hub and the outer rim of the Wheel, influence all the others parts of life and together form a cluster of wellness that we call Life with God.

Relational, Intellectual and Emotional Wellness form a second cluster of closely related topics that together address the various aspects of Life in Community: in our homes, our neighborhoods, our congregations and in team ministries.

You may find that your work on Vocational Wellness will be closely tied to the Physical and Financial aspects of life. Together the three form a cluster we call Life in Ministry, because we're only able to engage fully in our Vocational callings when we experience a satisfying foundation of Physical and Financial wholeness.

Wherever you begin your wellness journey, The Wellness Wheel is intended as a guide to help you answer the question, "How am I doing?" As you journey with Jesus to find his healing touch in your Vocational life, don't be surprised to discover how closely it is tied to your Physical and Financial wellbeing, and all the other aspects of your life too! You've chosen a wonderful place to begin. Trust the process you'll find in this Workbook. God is always ready to pour out his gifts into your life for restoration and renewal.

And when the time is right, our resources to guide your wellness journey in other new directions will be ready for you!

The "Reclaiming the Joy of Ministry" Workbook Series

I hope you agree that following Jesus into a life of Christian ministry is the greatest adventure in the kingdom of God. I expect you've also discovered how hard it can be. Richly rewarding? Yes, it is. Tremendously demanding? Absolutely!

The Prophets and Apostles all experienced both the joys and the struggles of ministry. Even before God invited Elijah to join him on a wellness retreat, the Lord's called church workers have been learning the lessons of preventive self-care. God's desire for you is effectiveness and longevity in ministry. The "Reclaiming the Joy of Ministry" Workbook Series is designed to help you learn to apply the unique wellness practices that will ensure a long and joyful career in ministry.

The Bible is our only norm and guide for God's perfect plan of salvation and also for the life of Christian living that follows redemption in Christ. At Grace Place Wellness Ministries, we have often turned to Paul's Letter to the Ephesians. In the first three chapters, the gospel of saving grace in Jesus is beautifully outlined. God's purpose is revealed: "... to bring all things in heaven and one earth together under one head, even Christ" (1:10). The gospel is proclaimed: "For it is by grace you have been saved, through faith – and this is not from yourselves, it is the gift of God – not by works, so that no one can boast" (2:8-9). God's wish for power and love in his children is affirmed: "And I pray that you, being rooted and established in love, may have power, together with all the saints, to grasp how wide and long and high and deep is the love of Christ, and to know this love that surpasses all knowledge – that you may be filled to the measure of all the fullness of God" (3:17-19).

Chapters four through six of Ephesians are not a sudden shift to an ethical section of demands for holy living, but a continuation of the gospel flow of the opening chapters. It's by the power of the grace of God that Paul can urge us to do what we could never do under our own power. "As a prisoner for the Lord, then, I urge you to live a life worthy of the calling you have received" (4:1). Impossible? On our own, Yes! But the apostle continues, "To each of us grace has been given as Christ apportioned it" (4:7). Only by the grace of Christ are we able "to put off your old self, which is being corrupted by its deceitful desires; to be made new in the attitude of your minds; and to put on the new self, created to be like God in true righteousness and holiness" (4:22-24).

Your wellness journey, discovering God's intention for "all the fullness of Christ" in you, is a journey of grace, welcoming and receiving God's work by the Holy Spirit through Word and Sacrament, making you new in the attitude of your mind, leading you to Spirit-led behaviors of vitality and joy.

Hopefully, your study of our book "Reclaiming the Joy of Ministry: The Grace Place Way to Church Worker Wellness" has informed you of the threats to wellness that church workers and their families face every day. I hope it has also inspired you to tackle this next phase of your wellness journey. The Ten Lessons that form the outline of the book form the foundation of your preparation for developing a wellness plan of your own. The Ten Lessons are...

1. Ministry is great, but hard
2. Because ministry is the way of the cross
3. And overwhelmed is a way of life
4. So don't try this alone.
5. Joy is fuel for ministry
6. But ministry threatens the joy of life with God
7. And ministry threatens the joy of life in community
8. And ministry threatens the joy of life in ministry
9. Which makes daily healing essential
10. Therefore, self-care has to be intentional.

That's the bottom line: Self-care has to be intentional. The "Reclaiming the Joy of Ministry" Workbook is your guide for that intentional preventive self-care effort.

We encourage you to keep three images in mind along the way; one from the Old Testament, one from the New Testament and one from contemporary life.

The first is Elijah's collapse and restoration. Imagine his journey from the joy of Mount Carmel to the depths of despair under the broom tree, then on to the Mountain of the Lord, and finally back into ministry. Listen to the Lord say, "Elijah, go back the way you came!" (1 Kings 19:15). This is the picture of HOPE. You're in good company with the thousands of ministers and their families who learned how hard ministry can be, but who have been renewed for continued service by the grace of God in Christ, (with a little guidance and encouragement from Grace Place Wellness Ministries!)

The second image to keep in mind is that of Paul and Silas in Philippi. "After they had been severely flogged..." (Acts 16:23), how did they respond? They spent the night in prayer with songs of celebration. This is the picture of JOY. God's design for everyone in ministry is that in spite of the hardships, the joy of the Lord would be their fuel for ministry and their constant companion.

The third image is that of the airline flight attendant giving instructions on the proper use of the oxygen mask. "If you're traveling with others who need your assistance, be sure to secure your own oxygen mask firmly in place before attending to their needs." This is the picture of intentionality. Self-care is not selfish when the purpose is the wellbeing of others who depend on you and who need you at your best.

We like the oxygen mask illustration because it so clearly describes the wellness journey as both personal and corporate. You'll be developing a wellness action plan that is personal; tailored to fit your personality, history, experiences, preferences, learning style and passions. Only you can design your plan because you are the world's foremost authority on you! But it's also corporate. Your wellness as a minister of the gospel is not for your own sake, but for the sake of those whom you have been called to serve. It's why you put your own oxygen mask on first, for the sake of those traveling with you who need your assistance.

Early on in this workbook you'll recognize my background as an ordained minster of The Lutheran Church Missouri Synod. Martin Luther made more than his share of blunders in his walk of faith and service. I'm convinced that his understanding of the enormity of the power of the gospel to heal and to save comes from his inability to overcome his failures by his own wisdom and strength. He knew the greatness of God so well because he knew his own weakness. That puts me in good company. I find in Luther's thought and in the Confessional writings of the Lutheran Church great wisdom for any disciple of Jesus seeking a fuller and richer life of faith and service. (It's also the doctrinal material I know the best, so naturally I quote it the most!) If you are from a different Christian tradition, I trust you to apply these lessons from your own theological perspective, but I believe you'll find Luther's insight helpful.

The professional church workers of The LCMS are categorized as either "Ordained" or "Commissioned" ministers: ordained pastors and other commissioned ministerial offices adjunct to the pastoral office such as Deaconesses, Parochial School Teachers, Directors of Christian Education, Music and Outreach, etc. Your faith tradition may define these roles differently. Throughout the "Reclaiming the Joy of Ministry" Workbook I'll most often use the term "ministers" to refer to the broad spectrum of professional church workers. Predominantly, we'll be talking about pastors because the research on church worker wellness is almost exclusively focused on pastors and their families, but is nearly always applicable to other church work professionals. When appropriate, I'll mention parish pastors specifically. I hope you'll be able to translate my imperfect phraseology and the guidance contained here to relate to your own situation.

Spouses of church workers play a critical role in the wellbeing of their beloved. Minister's wives and husbands are often more attuned to the stresses that their loved ones are enduring than the workers are themselves. I strongly encourage you to make your spouse a partner in your growth process outlined in "Reclaiming the Joy." It could just as easily be titled, "Reclaiming *Our* Joy." If you are married to a minister, I consider you a partner in our effort at Grace Place Wellness Ministries to (as they say on the airliner) get those oxygen masks firmly planted on the faces of those on whom we all depend! God bless you as you offer encouragement, guidance and a sense of urgency to the one you love to find the grace they need.

You might be diving into this workbook because you're in need of renewal and healing; maybe life in ministry has left you depleted. Or you might be here to learn new practices that will sustain your vitality and joy in ministry for the long haul. My experience with thousands of ministers over the years suggests that you might need a little bit of both. Either way, you're on the right road. It's a road that leads to renewed vitality and joy in ministry for your personally, but also to a congregation as you lead from a healthier place.

Wellness is a journey not a destination. Commenting on the Parable of the Leaven, Martin Luther once wrote,

The new leaven is the faith and grace of the Spirit. It does not leaven the whole lump at once, but gently, and gradually, we become like this new leaven and eventually, a bread of God. This life, therefore, is not godliness but the process of becoming godly, not health but getting well, not being but becoming, not rest but exercise. We are not now what we shall be, but we are on the way. The process is not yet finished, but it is actively going on. This is not the goal but it is the right road. At present, everything does not gleam and sparkle, but everything is being cleansed.[1]

The process that you will encounter in each Step of "Reclaiming the Joy" is designed to lead you on a pathway from your current situation to a new, more vibrant and more joyful state by welcoming the healing touch of God the Holy Spirit.

Health and Joy!

Rev. Dr. Darrell W. Zimmerman
Grace Place Wellness Ministries
www.GracePlaceWellness.org

1 Martin Luther, *Defense and Explanation of All the Articles*, Luther's Works: American Edition, Vol. 32, (Philadelphia: Fortress, 1958), p. 24.

Using the Vocational Wellness Workbook

Just as is the case in our whole life in Christ, so also on this journey the process of healing and the process of learning new wellness habits can take time. As the Lord works in you through his Word of law, pointing out your unhealthy choices and creating dissatisfaction with your current state, and as he works in you through his Word of gospel, granting healing, and guiding you in new, healthier directions, you will experience numerous times of both frustration and gladness, of confession and forgiveness, of struggle and celebration. That's the way it has always been for those whom their loving Father is teaching and disciplining.

To a large degree, church worker wellness is about identity in Christ. Confusion over identity in Christ is a common problem among professional church workers. Ministers proclaim the gospel of grace apart from good works, but work as if their salvation depended on ministry "success." Clarity comes when we remember that we live out what it means to be humans under God's grace in two different dimensions of life. Martin Luther called these two dimensions "two kinds of righteousness." The first is a passive righteousness where we are merely receivers of the work of God to wash away sin and grant the gift of life eternal. Think of this passive righteousness as vertical, defining life with God. The second is an active righteousness, the horizontal life of love and service toward neighbor. Here we cooperate with God as he guides us into new behavior, blessing us with forgiveness and also strength for new obedience.

Healing is never a work we do in ourselves. The Grace Place Model is not a self-help plan, but a journey to that place of grace under the care of a loving God who has plans for you in his kingdom's work! We encourage you to take your time on this journey to wholeness; these things can rarely be rushed. Some parts of the journey will need more time than others. You may need to take detours along the way, but for the sake of your own joy in ministry and the benefit of those who need your faithful service, continue to work the plan. Thousands and thousands of your fellow servants of the gospel, dating all the way back to Elijah, have found refreshment and renewal from a God who binds up the wounded and sends them back into joyful service once again.

You'll be tempted to rush your wellness journey, but please consider the wisdom that Jesus offered his disciples. "This is what the kingdom of God is like. A man scatters seed on the ground. Night and day, whether he sleeps or gets up, the seed sprouts and grows, though he does not know how. All by itself the soil produces grain—first the stalk, then the head, then the full kernel in the head. As soon as the grain is ripe, he puts the sickle to it, because the harvest has come" (Mark 4:26-29). God works most naturally through organic processes. Our current situations are usually the end result of the lifelong journeys that led us to where we are today.

Life and growth are journeys that take time. We strongly encourage you to consider this workbook as a guide for an adventure of discovery, of learning new habits and making new commitments to your own wellbeing. It's a journey that is much more like a crock pot than a microwave. These things take time. Life in Christ is always more about becoming than it is about arriving. Be patient with yourself. Rely on God's grace first, and learn to be gracious to yourself also. Commit to the process outlined in the five Steps in this workbook, and give time for the Holy Spirit to work according to his perfect timing, not your own.

Each of the eight workbooks for each of the eight aspects of wellness in the "Reclaiming the Joy" series are broken down into five separate Steps, the same steps you will follow as you address the issue of Vocational wellness.

In Step One you will be introduced to some of the key elements of the Grace Place Wellness model that thousands of others have learned since our first retreat in the fall of 2000. You'll spend some time considering the nature of Vocational wellness as depicted in the scriptures. You will be encouraged to consider a simple Marker of Wellbeing and to examine your own walk of faith by the fruit of the Spirit. In particular, you'll be asked to identify the sources of joy that you experience in this aspect of your walk with God and your walk with others.

In Step Two you'll be challenged to consider what has become broken in your Vocational life. Why has this become that part of your journey that is in need of the Lord's gracious, healing touch? What forces around you, and which choices that you've made, have contributed to the depletion of your joy and the discomfort you're currently enduring? What forces at work in your life are motivating you to establish wiser, healthier practices into your Vocational life? You'll be asked to define your current reality by clearly articulating what's going on in your heart, your mind and your spirit. This will prepare you to seek the renewal that God is always ready to offer his children.

Step Three will help you to envision the desired future condition you seek, by the grace of God through his healing care. Through consideration of biblical examples and remembering your own personal history of blessedness under God's providential care, you will start to define what Vocational wellness might look like for you. You'll also begin to count the costs involved in making new choices that will open you to new beginnings, putting off the old nature, being made new in Christ, and putting on the new nature to walk by the Spirit (Ephesians 4:22-24), renewed and refreshed for days ahead.

In Step Four you will be guided through a planning process to help you begin to eliminate or at least manage the forces that are contributing to your brokenness. You'll set goals to help you seek out the healing care that God provides in the gospel resources of Word and Sacrament and in your communities of care and encouragement. You'll consider what resources of nurture and blessing you will need along the journey as you walk by faith, never perfectly healed, but bound and fortified for the next phase of your journey.

In Step Five you will develop a plan for the ongoing wellness practices that will sustain you with vitality and joy in ministry. While the disciplines of self-care are timeless and common to all disciples, your history, learning style and attitudes are unique, so you'll design your own program of preventive self-care, one that suits you best. You'll also consider ways to turn your new behaviors into lifelong wellness habits.

A wellness journey is always personal, but never private. In Steps Three, Four and Five, you'll be challenged to invite other members of the Body of Christ to come alongside to offer wisdom and encouragement. People resources that have proven very helpful to others include

- **Coach** – to ask challenging questions to keep you accountable
- **Mentor** – to be a trusted sounding board and source of advice
- **Counselor** – to help you discover new perspectives on your situation
- **Spiritual Director** – to help you explore current or new spiritual disciplines
- **Peer Group** – to join you on your wellness journey

You'll also be asked to consider accessing the many community resources available to you who are interested in your wellbeing. These could include congregational resources, guidance from your ministerial association, your denominational offices or other professional services available in your community.

For additional encouragement to utilize the many people resources who are invested in and dependent on your wellness, be sure to review Lesson Four from *Reclaiming the Joy of Ministry*, "Don't Try this Alone."

We're confident that as you humbly seek the mercy and strength of your loving Father in heaven, he will bless you with every good gift of healing and wisdom as you walk by faith under his abiding care!

Reclaiming the Joy of Ministry: Vocational Wellness

A WORD FROM THE LORD

Then I heard the voice of the Lord saying, "Whom shall I send? And who will go for us?" And I said, "Here am I. Send me!" Isaiah 6:8

A WORD FROM LUTHER

"Our Lord God fills His high office in an odd manner. He entrusts it to preachers, poor sinners, who tell and teach the message and yet live according to it only in weakness. Thus God's power always goes forward amid extreme weakness."[2] Martin Luther

A WORD OF WISDOM

"The place God calls you is the place where your deep gladness and the world's hunger meet."[3] Frederick Buechner

The Marker of Vocational Wellbeing

As I grow in God's grace of Vocational Gentleness, I am finding joy in Humility as I serve through my calling and gifts.

2 Ewald M. Pless, ed., *What Luther Says Volume 2*, (St. Louis: Concordia, 1959), p. 950.
3 Frederick Buechner, *Wishful Thinking: A Seeker's ABCs*, (San Francisco: Harper, 1993), p. 119.

Understanding Vocational Wellness

This Step requires considerable time for slow reflection and contemplation and should not be rushed. Make a commitment to trust the process outlined in this Step. Make a note of your starting date and also note reminders in your calendar to check your faithfulness to the process every few weeks.

Starting Date_____ Dates to assess progress_____

PRAYER FOR THE JOURNEY

You won't actively engage with this process every day, but you can seek the Lord's blessing constantly. How will you remind yourself to pray for your wellness journey daily? Make note of your plan for prayer here and also in your devotional Bible or your prayer journal.

SELECTING PRIORITY ACTIVITIES

Briefly preview the suggested activities for Step One. Will you complete all or only some of the activities?

Essential – Which of the activities listed do you consider essential for your growth in understanding the biblical design for Vocational wellness?

Other – What other activities that are not listed might be helpful as you seek to gain a better understanding of Vocational wellness?

VOCATIONAL WELLNESS IN ONE WORD: HUMILITY

The call of God into a life of ministry still rings out today, just as it did centuries ago. "Then I heard the voice of the Lord saying, 'Whom shall I send? And who will go for us?' And I said, 'Here am I. Send me!'" (Isaiah 6:8). Vocational Humility is joyfully following God's call into kingdom service, utilizing the gifts he has given in a spirit of Christ's own Gentleness and service, humbled at the thought of representing Almighty God to the world, just as Isaiah was long ago.

Ministry in the Christian church has a way of humbling a person. That's okay, because humble is a good place to be. How many times do we read in the scriptures about an initial response to God's call sounding something like, "You've got the wrong person!"? Moses said, "Try my brother. He'd be much better at this!" Esther said, "Seriously? My only qualification is that I won a beauty contest!" Peter said, "Go away from me, Lord; I'm a sinful man!" In each case, the Lord's response was, "I'm glad to hear you say that. Now I've got you in a place where I can actually use you."

C. S. Lewis said of the truly humble person, "He will not be thinking about Humility; he will not be thinking about himself at all."[4] Servants of Christ recognize their inadequacy for the task, but trust confidently that the God who calls will also supply what we need. Self-care is not selfish when our purpose is to be at our best in order to offer our best service to others. Vocational wellbeing begins with the kind of Humility that says, "I have nothing to offer these people, Lord, so I'm turning to you to fill me with all I need to serve: faith, passion, strength, joy and hope to face the challenges before me."

Take a few moments to reflect on the wondrous and humbling gift of this call into ministry as depicted in Luther's Sacristy Prayer.

"Lord God, You have appointed me in the church as bishop and pastor. You see how unfit I am to attend to such a great and difficult office, and if it had not been for Your help, I would long since have ruined everything. Therefore I call upon You.

"Of course, I want to put my mouth and heart to use. I shall teach the people, and I myself shall learn and shall meditate diligently on Your Word. Use me as Your instrument. Only do not forsake me; for if I am alone, I shall easily destroy everything."

Record your thoughts here.

---

4 C. S. Lewis, *Mere Christianity*, (New York: Macmillan, 1952) p. 114.

BIBLICAL REFLECTIONS ON HUMILITY

Read each of the passages listed and make note of the key lesson about Humility from each. Circle five or six for more careful study.

Deuteronomy 8 – Israel is trained in Humility
Key Lesson

1 Kings 3:1-15 – Solomon asks for wisdom
Key Lesson

2 Chronicles 7:11-22 – Solomon is advised to seek Humility
Key Lesson

Proverbs 16:18-20 – Pride goes before destruction
Key Lesson

Micah 6:6-8 – Walk humbly with your God
Key Lesson

Matthew 18:1-6 – The greatest in the kingdom of heaven
Key Lesson

Matthew 23 – Seven woes for teachers of the law
Key Lesson

Acts 20:17-38 – Paul and the Ephesian Elders
Key Lesson

2 Corinthians 12:1-10 A thorn in the flesh
Key Lesson

Colossians 3:12-17 – Clothe yourselves with Humility
Key Lesson

James 4 – Humble leadership
Key Lesson

1 Peter 5:1-10 – Shepherds of God's flock
Key Lesson

List here other scriptures on Humility related to Vocational wellness that come to mind.
Summarize what the scriptures teach about Humility in ministry.

# THE HEART OF THE ISSUE

Life in ministry is a difficult balancing act. On the one hand, it takes a kind of "holy hubris" to accept the call into ministry and say, "I represent the Lord God Almighty! What I say to you, I speak on his behalf!" Without boldness of heart and confidence in the call, no one could ever consider a life in ministry (see Jeremiah 1:4-10). On the other hand, as Luther so eloquently expressed, none of us are qualified or equipped for the task. A life of ministry is a life of service, the life of a slave (see Luke 17:5-10). Humble dependence on the Lord is essential in ministry. When Paul wrote a very confrontational letter to the Corinthians, he displayed the proper balance of holy hubris and heartfelt Humility, keeping them in a dynamic tension. "By the meekness and Gentleness of Christ, I appeal to you – I, Paul, who am 'timid' when face to face with you, but 'bold' when away!" (2 Corinthians 10:1). Paul went on in this chapter to clearly present his credentials as a genuine, called Apostle of Christ. That takes boldness. He also reminded the church that his service to them was always in a spirit of Humility and Gentleness (see 2 Corinthians 11). In the balancing act of hubris and Humility, we always err on the side of Humility.

The temptation to get this wrong is our constant companion. Ministerial pride, considering ourselves to be different, more spiritual or more holy than others, can jump up and bite us at any moment. The Barna Group's research on pastors indicates the greatest causes of pastoral frustration: "1. Lack of commitment among laypeople (35%), 2. Low level of spiritual maturity among churchgoers (27%)." Is it possible that church workers become frustrated because they place unreasonable expectations on the members of the congregation? It's a dangerous Vocational pitfall to think that the minister is more highly committed and more spiritually mature than any other member of the church.

The balancing act of the sanctified hubris of the office you hold and the sincere Humility essential to faithful service is a continual challenge.

What signs in your own life indicate that you are managing the balancing act well?

What signs indicate that you have not managed it well?

C REFLECTION ON THE MARKER

A Marker is an indicator along the journey that you are making progress in the right direction. Each of the Markers in the "Reclaiming the Joy of Ministry" series includes the fruit of the Spirit (Galatians 5) related to the aspect of wellness, joy which is the overall indicator of wellness, a one word description of the heart of wellness for that aspect, and a reference to Ephesians chapter four, all of which will be examined in closer detail in the Steps that follow.

The Marker of Vocational Wellbeing

As I grow in God's grace of Vocational GENTLENESS, I am finding
joy in Humility as I serve through my calling and gifts.

Take a few moments to reflect on this short definition of a balanced, joyful life in ministry.

Circle the words or phrases that are most meaningful to you and explain why in the space below.

Place a question mark by words or phrases that need clarification.

What would you add to this indicator of Vocational wellness that's missing?

 **LESSON NINE ASSESSMENTS**

Review the assessments of wellness from Lesson Nine of "Reclaiming the Joy of Ministry: The Grace Place Way to Church Worker Wellness." What did you learn about yourself that directed you to this study of Vocational wellness?

 SCRIPTURE STUDY ON VOCATIONAL WELLNESS

When you were considering God's call into ministry which scripture passages gave you the clearest guidance? List them here with notes about what they meant to you.

Read each of the passages listed and make note of the key lesson about Vocational wellness from each. Circle five or six for more careful study.

1 Kings 19:15 – God sends Elijah back into ministry
Key Lesson

Matthew 10 - Jesus sends the 12
Key Lesson

Matthew 25:14-30 - The Parable of the Talents
Key Lesson

Mark 10:35-45 - Servant Leadership
Key Lesson

Luke 10:1-24 - Joy in Ministry
Key Lesson

John 13:12-17 - Jesus washes the disciples' feet
Key Lesson

Acts 2:42-47 - The early church in humble service
Key Lesson

Acts 4:32-37 - The first Christians together in love
Key Lesson

Acts 6:1-7 - Humble, Spirit-filled servants
Key Lesson

Acts 16:16-34 - Paul and Silas in the Philippian Jail
Key Lesson

1 Corinthians 9 - Your faithful service changes lives
Key Lesson

Ephesians 6:7 - Serving the Lord, not men
Key Lesson

Ephesians 6:10-19 - The Whole Armor of God
Key Lesson

1 Timothy 3 - Qualifications of an Elder
Key Lesson

2 Timothy 2:15 - A worker approved by God
Key Lesson

Titus 1 - Qualifications of an Elder
Key Lesson

1 Peter 4 - Suffering servants of Christ
Key Lesson

Which other scriptures related to Vocational wellness come to mind?

Summarize what the scriptures teach about Vocational wellness.

F JESUS AND VOCATIONAL WELLNESS

Jesus lived the perfect life of a humble servant. Which stories from the gospels best exemplify for you our Lord's pattern of Vocational wellness?

G THE FRUIT OF THE SPIRIT IS GENTLENESS

"Those who have received the Spirit are to live by the received Spirit and reach out for the charismatic gifts that are needed for service in the church and to the world."[5]

The Christian life is lived in the power of the Holy Spirit, through the gifts he imparts. The multi-faceted fruit of the Spirit includes the gift of Gentleness, which seems to have a natural link to our lives of Vocational Humility.

The following notes are intended to invite you to an extended time of Bible study and reflection on this aspect of the Spirit's fruit in your own life.

BIBLE STUDY ON GENTLENESS

Gentleness, *praütēs* in Greek, is etymologically related to "friend," connoting a relationship that is gentle, pleasant, affable and mild, as opposed to one that is rough, hard, brutal, or angry.[6]

In Ephesians 4:2, *praütēs* is the calling of all servants of Christ. Commenting on Ephesians 4:2 "Be completely humble and gentle; be patient, bearing with one another in love," Thomas Winger says, "The common thread in both 'Humility' and 'meekness' [*praütēs*] is the Spirit-wrought gift of Christlike Humility."[7] The quality of Gentleness is distributed from God to those who represent him. Jesus had it (Matthew 11:29); it was his gift to the apostle Paul (2 Corinthians 10:1); Paul encouraged it in the lives of other church workers, like Timothy (2 Timothy 2:25), and all who have followed in his footsteps.

How is Gentleness practically applied in church leadership? Galatians 6 explains that the Humility of Gentleness is on display in the boldness of confronting sin in an erring disciple. "Brothers, if someone is caught in a sin, you who are spiritual should restore him gently [praütēs]" (Galatians 6:1).

What do each of the following teach you about the Holy Spirit's fruit of Gentleness?

Matthew 11:29

5 Edmund Schlink, *Baptism*, (St. Louis: Concordia, 1972) p. 70, emphasis added.
6 Gerhard Kittel, ed, *Theological Dictionary of the New Testament*, vol. VI (Grand Rapids: Eerdmans, 1968), p. 645.
7 Thomas Winger, *Ephesians*, (St. Louis: Concordia, 2015) p. 429.

Bible study on gentleness

Colossians 3:12

1 Thessalonians 2:7

2 Timothy 2:25

Titus 3:2

James 1:21

James 3:13

Psalm 18:35

Summarize here what you've discovered or rediscovered about the Spirit's gift of Gentleness.

The Fruit of the Spirit is, in Galatians 5:22-23, a singular gift; it's not "fruits" of the Spirit, but a many-faceted gift that includes Gentleness. What might the other facets of this fruit in your life contribute to your Vocational wellness? How might the Spirit of God bring you healing and sustain you in ministry through his fruit of love, joy, peace, patience, kindness, goodness, faithfulness, Gentleness and self-control?

H The Joy of Gentleness: How Joy Flows from This Fruit

Take a little time to reflect on Lesson Five, "Joy Fuels Ministry," from "Reclaiming the Joy of Ministry." What were the most important things you learned about Christian joy?

Joy does not come from doing gentle things, but from being a gentle person. The great hymn of Philippians 2 calls disciples of Jesus to have the same attitude, the same mindset, as their Lord. He lived his mission as a humble and gentle servant, caring compassionately for all in their time of need. The only time that Jesus is recorded as saying that his actions were "an example" to the disciples was when he washed their feet on Maundy Thursday (John 13:15). Shortly thereafter, our Suffering Servant Lord willingly and without complaint poured out his life for our salvation. Very few would interpret the call of Jesus to wash feet only in its literal sense. His call is more importantly a summons to a transformed attitude, a heart melted by his own perfect love. It's a gift that only the Lord himself can impart: Gentleness.

From a gentle spirit flow naturally gentle acts. Only then, from acts of genuine gentle service and love does joy flow freely to both the receiver and the giver. Paul continues in Philippians 2 with this encouragement, "Do everything without complaining or arguing," and he concludes the call to gentle service by saying that even though his life is being poured out in his gospel service, "I am glad and rejoice with all of you. So you too should be glad and rejoice with me" (Philippians 2:14, 17-18). "Christian joy is a good feeling in the soul, produced by the Holy Spirit, as he causes us to see the beauty of Christ in the Word and in the world" (John Piper). Sacrificial service offered in Gentleness and Humility results in joy.

Reflect on this definition of the Spirit's gift of joy:

"Christian joy is a good feeling in the soul produced by the Holy Spirit as he causes us to see the beauty of Christ in the Word and in the world." John Piper[8]

What brings you the greatest joy in ministry?

What diminishes your joy?

In recent days, how have you witnessed the beauty of Christ through your vocation? What happened? What was your initial reaction? How did it affect your passion for your call? How has the experience lingered in your heart and mind?

n recent days, what conversation, Vocational experience or disappointment has diminished your oy? Describe here how the experience has lingered in your heart and mind.

1 HYMN/SONG THAT EXPRESSES THE JOY OF VOCATIONAL GENTLENESS

Which songs or hymns could enhance your devotional life during your time of study on Vocational Gentleness?

8 John Piper, www.desiringgod.org/articles/how-do-you-define-joy July 25, 2015.

SUMMARY CONCLUSION OF STEP ONE: HUMILITY AND GENTLENESS IN MINISTRY

It's time to pull all of your thoughts together. Look back over your study in Step One. Can you summarize what you've learned so far about the nature of Vocational wellness in a few short sentences? Be sure to review the Marker of Wellness from the beginning of this Step. Based on what you've learned, would you state it differently now?

Make note here of the key learnings from your reflection and study in this Step. These will give shape and direction to the process in the next Step, and you will refer back to this list later.

Step Two
Understanding Vocational Brokenness

This Step requires considerable time for slow reflection and contemplation and should not be rushed. Make a commitment to trust the process outlined in this Step. Make a note of your starting date and also note reminders in your calendar to check your faithfulness to the process every few weeks.

Starting Date_____   Dates to assess progress_____

PRAYER FOR THE JOURNEY

How have the lessons of Step One changed the focus of your prayer for the wellness journey?

How will you remember to stay active in prayer for this next part of your discovery process? Make note of your plan for prayer here and near your devotional reading Bible.

SELECTING PRIORITY ACTIVITIES

Briefly preview the suggested activities for Step Two of the Workbook. Will you complete all or only some of the activities?

Essential – Which of the activities listed do you consider essential for your growth in understanding the biblical design for Vocational wellness?

Other – What other activities that are not listed might be helpful as you seek to gain a better understanding of Vocational wellness?

REVIEW "RECLAIMING THE JOY OF MINISTRY"

Take some time to review what the Bible says about the way of the
cross as outlined in Lesson Two of "Reclaiming the Joy of Ministry" and
the research on church worker wellness from Lesson Eight. List here
the three most enlightening topics from Lesson Eight.

 ## SELF-ASSESSMENT

Take the Vocational Wellness Assessment you first saw in Lesson Nine of "Reclaiming the Joy of
Ministry" over again.

VOCATIONAL WELLBEING (Almost Never 1 2 3 4 5 6 Almost Always)

_____ I am regularly experiencing the joy of Gentleness in my life of service.
Why did you mark the score that you did? What is that score telling you?

_____ God's call to a life of service is an ever-increasing source of Humility.
Why did you mark the score that you did? What is that score telling you?

_____ I am often able to recognize ways that God uses me to build up the body of Christ.
Why did you mark the score that you did? What is that score telling you?

_____ Total Vocational
How did your Total Vocational score compare to the other aspects of wellness?

C HEALTHY/UNHEALTHY SCALE

Take the assessment from Lesson Nine on the Vocational Healthy/Unhealthy scale over again.

HEALTHY							UNHEALTHY
Passion-driven	6	5	4	3	2	1	Job Description driven
Spirit-led	6	5	4	3	2	1	Ego-led
Joyful	6	5	4	3	2	1	Burdensome
Boundaries	6	5	4	3	2	1	Overfunctioning
Energized	6	5	4	3	2	1	Burnt out
Gitta	6	5	4	3	2	1	Gotta
Servant	6	5	4	3	2	1	Authority

_____Total Vocational

What are you learning about your Vocational wellness?

D #1 INDICATOR OF VOCATIONAL BROKENNESS: DIMINISHED JOY

It is the almost universal experience of ministers to endure at least one significant period of frustration due to the enormous challenges of ministry; most ministers experience such periods of Vocational brokenness numerous times throughout their careers. Vocational wellness is learning to manage the times of distress through renewal of their calling and learning to rediscover the joy of sharing the gospel of Christ. "Every pastor, regardless of church size or job satisfaction, has frustrations related to the daily reality of congregational life. And that's okay. The trick is to acknowledge irritations without letting them fill one's field of vision. When frustrations get too big or too close, they distort perception and make daily joys appear small and inconsequential – which is an apt description of burnout."[9]

Therapist Bev Yahnke says, "Many pastors I've spoken with have reported that, when taken captive by burnout, depression or anxiety, their first response was to redouble their churchly efforts to ensure that no one would know they were struggling. Others have shared that, in light of Jesus' words about joy in the Christian life (John 15:11), their own experience of sadness and emptiness in ministry left them feeling guilt, shame or fear that they had failed."[10]

Write a paragraph about a time when you were one of those people Dr. Yahnke describes.

9 Barna Group, The State of Pastors: How Today's Faith Leaders Are Navigating Life and Leadership in an Age of Complexity, (Barna Group, 2017), p. 101. 10 Bev Yahnke: "Mental Health and Pastoral Ministry" Lutheran Witness/October (2018)

Pastor Howard-John Wesley, in announcing an upcoming sabbatical to his congregation, said, "There's a weight a pastor bears in their soul and their emotions that is inescapable. There's not been a day in these past eleven years that I have not woken up and knew that there's something I had to do for the church, that I have to be available for a call, that I journey with people through the highs and the lows of life, through the great moments of celebration and in the valley of death." How would you describe to a trusted friend the daily weight of the burdens of Christian ministry?

There are many clinical definitions of burnout, but the definition we like best is very simple:

Burnout is when the body is doing the work but the spirit is absent.

What rings true in this definition?

How might you describe burnout differently?

Signs of vocational burnout can include such things as fatigue, loss of motivation, health problems, negativity, diminished sense of satisfaction, and poor performance of daily tasks. When was a time from your past that you were most concerned that you were in danger of burnout?

Can you remember the assets that helped you to endure and come through this difficult time?

What indicators, if any, are you experiencing that might show you are currently in a time of burnout or that you might be entering a period of burnout?

REACH OUT FOR IMMEDIATE SUPPORT: If you are experiencing the symptoms of burnout, or are concerned that you might be close, help is available to you. It's critically important that you reach out for assistance. Your health insurance card in most cases has the phone number of the Employee Assistance Program which you should call immediately. Your closest friends will be greatly appreciative when you call on them for support, counsel and encouragement. Your peers in ministry are a fellowship of support for you. Your district office or other judicatory has resources for your care in time of need. These and other resources are available for your immediate support because you have earned them, and because you and the many, many others in your situation deserve every form of assistance you may need.

⚡ #2 INDICATOR OF VOCATIONAL BROKENNESS: CHURCH WORKERS ARE LEAVING THE MINISTRY

Within just a few years of commissioning or ordination, nearly every church worker can tell stories of classmates who have left the ministry.

"The first perhaps most consequential result of inadequate care for ministers is that they leave the ministry of the church. Plenty of research has explored the reasons why pastors leave the ministry and the results are widely varied and uneven, but a look at the research begins to paint a telling picture. One United Methodist study revealed that ten years after ordination, 41% had already left parish ministry, mostly for other areas of ministry, and at twenty years the number increased to 58%. An ELCA study showed that 15% of the 1988 graduating class had resigned or were removed from the roster within 13 years."[11]

Think back to your reaction the first time you heard of a classmate leaving the ministry. Do you know the reasons? How surprised were you to hear the news?

Who were you most surprised to learn about leaving the ministry?

Thoughts of changing vocation are very common among church workers. In the past twelve months, have you seriously considered leaving the ministry? If so, can you write down why you were thinking that way?

11 Cited in Hoge, Dean R. and Wenger, Jacqueline E., "Pastors in Transition: Why Clergy Leave Local Church Ministry," Eerdmans, Grand Rapids, 2005, p. 28.

ℱIDENTIFYING THE CAUSES OF VOCATIONAL BROKENNESS

Rate the following by how significantly they have contributed to your current dissatisfaction in your Vocational life.

Unreasonable Congregational Expectations Explicitly stated or implicitly implied descriptions of your responsibilities that are beyond your capacity. Expected mission success or ministry turn-arounds that would require super-human performance.
☐ High ☐ Medium ☐ Low

Unreasonable Personal Expectations The internal critique of negative self-talk. The inability to accept limitations of time, energy and resources to complete an unending harvest. Fear of being exposed as a phony if your human limits were known.
☐ High ☐ Medium ☐ Low

Lack of Identifiable Fruitfulness The results of gospel ministry are nearly always difficult to quantify in tangible fashion. Spiritual immaturity in others seems to rarely change. Attention to measurables (attendance, finances, etc.) for affirmation of success leads to frustration.
☐ High ☐ Medium ☐ Low

Vision Conflict Disagreement with congregational leadership about the objectives and expectations for the ministry. Your understanding of the nature of ministry does not match congregational expectations of the office.
☐ High ☐ Medium ☐ Low

Compassion Fatigue Giving more than you are receiving. A sense of diminishment, of being drained by the needs of others with little hope of your own replenishment. The demands of offering blessing to others without receiving the blessing of others.
☐ High ☐ Medium ☐ Low

Overfunctioning Working and serving beyond your physical, emotional, mental and spiritual capacity to serve. Lack of appropriate understanding of personal capacity and inadequate establishment of boundaries (work hours, days off, vacation, family time, recreation, etc.)
☐ High ☐ Medium ☐ Low

Personal Sacrifices Bitterness over the sacrifices (financial or otherwise) made for the sake of a calling into ministry. Resentment over the loss of personal freedoms that someone in your position may not enjoy publicly or even privately. Difficulty making close friendships.
☐ High ☐ Medium ☐ Low

Family Sacrifices Bitterness over the sacrifices (financial or otherwise) your family makes for the sake of your ministry. Resentment over the loss of personal freedoms that your family may not enjoy publicly or even privately. Your family's difficulty making close friendships.
☐ High ☐ Medium ☐ Low

Congregational Conflict Disagreement over ministry practices that diminish the joy of ministry. Long-standing congregational conflict and factions inherited from past generations. Hostility toward the church exhibited by the community or other churches.
☐ High ☐ Medium ☐ Low

Staff Conflict Breakdown of healthy relationships in team ministry. Disagreement between staff supervisors and subordinate team members. Division between church and school ministries. Poor communication and lack of trust in the ministry team.
☐ High   ☐ Medium   ☐ Low

Co-Dependency Unhealthy response to the troubles, needs or dependencies of others leads to self-destructive habits. Unwritten behavioral rules include the expectation of unhealthy levels of availability for others and heroic attempts at rescue. Guilt over inability to save others.
☐ High   ☐ Medium   ☐ Low

The Glittering Image The desire to "look good" to the public and to falsely represent the persona of having it all together personally, professionally and spiritually. Allowing placement upon the pedestal of recognition. The "Walk on Water" syndrome.
☐ High   ☐ Medium   ☐ Low

Comparisons to Predecessors Unflattering comparisons (likely inaccurate) to past holders of your office. Failure of members to grieve previous minister's departure. Unrelenting blame of current ministry struggles on your failure to exhibit the same gifts as your predecessor.
☐ High   ☐ Medium   ☐ Low

Confronting Sin The prophetic task of pursuing wandering sheep and confronting sin in their lives is extraordinarily demanding. No one enjoys it; failure to find support and time to adequately recover from confrontation can be debilitating.
☐ High   ☐ Medium   ☐ Low

Lack of Accountability Insufficient establishment of boundaries and procedures to monitor adherence to them. "Autonomous Christianity;" flying solo through the turbulent skies of ministry. Lack of safeguards against inappropriate behavior.
☐ High   ☐ Medium   ☐ Low

Rapid Rate of Change in the Church New generations with new expectations and demands for ministry. Outdated programs and skills result in a failure to meet ministry demands. Lack of continuing education. Technological expectations.
☐ High   ☐ Medium   ☐ Low

Rapid Rate of Change in the Culture Societal mores related to sexuality, marriage and family, tax exempt status, political activism, etc. Increasingly post-church culture. Church/state relationships nationally, regionally and locally.
☐ High   ☐ Medium   ☐ Low

Re-location Frequent moves take their toll on family life as we are forced to find new medical/dental practitioners, friends, schools, shopping, etc., and adjust to new customs, traditions, rituals and predecessors as well as a brand new "fishbowl."
☐ High   ☐ Medium   ☐ Low

Other? (Describe other contributing causes you are experiencing)

What is the primary cause of the Vocational anxiety you are currently experiencing?

List here the other most significant causes of brokenness from the list.

Describe the forces at work right now that are causing you discontent in your Vocational life.

9 NAMING MY VOCATIONAL STRUGGLE

We can never address an issue in our lives until we can accurately name it and identify its causes. The first step in the journey of healing and restored wellness is confession. In Step Three, you will begin to explore the Holy Spirit's intended work of restoration and healing in your life, but before embarking on that journey, it's important to know the place of your beginning.

Consider the following questions:

How are you feeling today because of the nature of your current Vocational reality?

How has your emotional, intellectual, relational and spiritual health been impacted by the Vocational struggles you are currently facing?

What are your fears, worries, anxieties about your current calling in ministry?

How have you experienced spiritual, emotional, relational, physical or financial pain because of the demands of this call?

How has your effectiveness in ministry been hindered?

What decisions and behaviors on your part have contributed to the stresses of your current situation?

How does your desire for continued growth and maturity as a child of God compel you to make changes in your behavior?

SELF-AWARENESS

Which inventories designed to give you greater self-awareness have been helpful to you in the past? What insight have you gained about your personality, character strengths and weaknesses, or other personal qualities through instruments like the Myers-Briggs Personality Type Indicator, the DiSC survey, the Enneagram or other similar tools?

How could you utilize your personal strengths to address some of the challenges you are currently facing?

How have your weaknesses contributed to your current situation or compounded your level of anxiety?

BIBLICAL EXAMPLES

Studying biblical examples of Vocational wellness can be helpful. What do you learn from Elijah (1 Kings 19), Jonah (Jonah 1-3), Timothy (1 Timothy and 2 Timothy) or Titus (Titus 1-3)?

PERSONAL EXAMPLES

Who do you know who has experienced a situation similar to yours? How might you approach that person about a conversation?

SUMMARY CONCLUSION OF STEP TWO: HOW AM I EXPERIENCING VOCATIONAL BROKENNESS?

As an exercise in reflection, use this space to draft a letter to a close friend or colleague (a real friend if it's more helpful, or an imagined friend) describing your current situation in ministry. (You can decide at a later date if it is appropriate and would be helpful for you to actually send the letter). Try to incorporate the various aspects of the Vocational wellness journey that you have experienced so far in this process.

Now it's time to pull all of your thoughts on Vocational brokenness together. Look back over your study in Step Two. Summarize what you've learned so far in a few short sentences.

Make note here of the key learnings from your reflection and study in this Step. These will give shape and direction to the process in the next Step.

JOIN THE GRACE PLACE WELLNESS COMMUNITY

It might be time for you to consider participating in the Grace Place Wellness Community, a gathering of like-minded church work professionals who are also on the wellness journey. Grace Place Wellness staff lead weekly conversations about health and wellness for the encouragement and support of people just like you. Join us – **www.community.graceplacewellness.org**

Understanding Vocational Healing

This Step requires considerable time for slow reflection and contemplation and should not be rushed. Make a commitment to trust the process outlined in this Step. Make a note of your starting date and also note reminders in your calendar to check your faithfulness to the process every few weeks.

Starting Date_____   Dates to assess progress_____

PRAYER FOR THE JOURNEY

How have the lessons of Step Two changed the focus of your prayer for the wellness journey?

How will you remember to stay active in prayer for this next part of your discovery process?

SELECTING PRIORITY ACTIVITIES

Briefly preview the suggested activities for Step Three of the workbook. Will you complete all or only some of the activities?

Essential – Which of the activities listed do you consider essential for your growth in understanding the biblical design for Vocational wellness?

Other – What other activities that are not listed might be helpful as you seek to gain a better understanding of Vocational wellness?

EPHESIANS 4:11-12

At Grace Place Wellness Ministries, we often refer to Ephesians 4 as a summary statement of the Bible's teaching on wellness because each of the eight aspects of wellness depicted in The Wellness Wheel are specifically addressed. The scriptures teach wellness for God's people on nearly every page. This chapter from Ephesians is not the Bible's whole teaching, but a simple launching pad for a more thorough study. We've identified this passage as an example of the Bible's teaching on Vocational wellness because it affirms the divine nature of the call into ministry. Confidence and security in the call from God is the foundation for a healthy ministry.

Read Ephesians 4:11-12 from your favorite translation.

What confidence do you find in knowing that Jesus is the Lord of the Church who sends people, (who sent you), into the harvest field?

What does it mean to you to be a gift from Jesus to his people, the Church? Be sure to spend adequate time reflecting on this important question.

How would you describe your call from God to a person who had never heard your story?

When did you first consider that God might be calling you to ministry?

Who were the influential people in helping you discern the call?

What gifts have you been given for ministry?

How have those gifts been affirmed by others?

When did you first begin to recognize those gifts?

What is it like when you are at your best, serving others through the gifts God has given?

The work of God in the lives of people is often hard to recognize, like seeds growing in a field (Mark 4:26-29). List some of the ways that God has used you in the past to build up his body, the Church? Give as many examples as you can. See if other examples come to mind in the days ahead.

Is God in this passage in any way calling you to repentance? If so, how will you respond?

Where do you find words of encouragement and blessing in this passage? Write those words on a note card and carry them with you in the days ahead.

Which other scripture passages affirm this message from God to you?

What commentaries or study helps will you consult to learn more from this passage?

Make note here of the word or phrase that has spoken most clearly to you in this study. How could that word be a source of the Spirit's gift of healing and renewal? Write here what the Spirit is teaching you about Vocational wellness.

seek the Lord's mercy & grace

₿ PAST HISTORY OF VOCATIONAL WELLNESS

Write a few paragraphs to complete the following: "I'm at my best Vocationally when..."

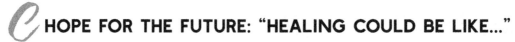

HOPE FOR THE FUTURE: "HEALING COULD BE LIKE..."

Take a moment to review Lesson Nine of "Reclaiming the Joy of Ministry" and the discussion on the healing work of the Holy Spirit in the lives of God's children. As you pause and seek the Lord's mercy and grace during a difficult time, what might it be like to know the healing touch of the gospel in your life? Letting the words flow freely as they come to you, write a paragraph or two that begins, "Healing could be like..."

𝒟 SUBSTANTIAL HEALING: THE DEVOTIONAL MODEL FROM "SCULPTOR SPIRIT"

God the Holy Spirit imparts wholeness to lives broken by the angry assaults of the devil, by a world spinning out of control and by the lusts of the flesh. God produces in them his fruit: love, joy, peace, patience, kindness, goodness, faithfulness, Gentleness and self-control. We highly recommend "Sculptor Spirit: Models of Sanctification from Spirit Christology" by Dr. Leopoldo Sánchez as a guide for the variety of ways that the Holy Spirit is active in the lives of God's people. Of the five models of sanctification discussed, the Devotional Model fits nicely with the topic of Vocational wellness, although the other models also offer guidance that may apply.

Sanchez says that the Devotional Model, "... deals with issues such as the need for balance and rhythm in life, avoiding the dangers of burnout and idleness, and inviting persons to stand still and rejoice in God's gifts of creation and salvation in a busy world,"[5] and specifically commends this model to church workers: "...this model can assist pastors and others in promoting among people a life of work, prayer, rest and play."[12] The best way to assist others is, of course, for ministers to model the model themselves!

Chapter Seven of "Sculptor Spirit" is the full consideration of the Devotional model. The following topics are raised for reflection on what the scriptures and the Church teach about the Spirit's work of renewal:

- God's creation of night and day for rest and for work.
- The dangerous polarities of giving too much or too little importance to work.
- The need inherent in all of God's creation for re-creation.
- Remembering that we were justified for work, not justified by works.
- Workaholics are idolaters.
- The blessedness of work and Spirit-led entrance into our work.
- We die to self to make room for God and trust him for results from our labors.

We strongly recommend that you set aside time for a study of this chapter from "Sculptor Spirit," or to reflect on these themes related to the Spirit's healing work in our lives for Vocational wellness.

---

12   Leopoldo A. Sánchez M. Sculptor Spirit: Models of Sanctification from Spirit Christology, (Downers Grove, IL: IVP Academic, 2019), p. 169.

Gospel Resources for Healing

The last exercise in this Step is to draft a compelling vision for Vocational wellness that, as best you are able, describes your desired future condition as you serve according to your gifts. The best vision for that desired future will be one that is bathed in prayer and guided by the direction of the Holy Spirit. Before you set about that important task of envisioning what life will be like when you experience Vocational renewal, consider an extended period of study and meditation using the following gospel based resources to fill your heart and mind with the Word of the Lord.

 PERSONAL READING LIST

Which books from your own library would be worth rediscovering as part of this process? List them here.

 SUGGESTED READING LIST FOR VOCATIONAL WELLNESS

Which books from the Grace Place Wellness reading list look intriguing to you? Circle the titles you will research and consider studying.

- C. F. W. Walther, *Church and Ministry*
- Henri Nouwen, *The Wounded Healer*
- David Keck, *Healthy Churches, Faithful Pastors*
- Bob Burns, *Resilient Ministry: What Pastors Told Us about Surviving and Thriving*
- Rae Jean, Proeschold-Bell, *Faithful and Fractured: Responding to the Clergy Health Crisis*
- Clay Werner, *On the Brink: Grace for the Burned-Out Pastor*
- Matt Bloom, *Flourishing in Ministry*
- Roy M. Oswald, *Clergy Self-Care: Finding a Balance for Effective Ministry*
- Jackson W. Carroll, *God's Potters: Pastoral Leadership and the Shaping of Congregations*
- Gary Harbaugh, *Pastor as Person*
- Paul David Tripp, *Dangerous Calling*
- Bob Burns, *Resilient Ministry*
- Eugene Peterson, *The Pastor*
- Eugene Peterson, *Five Smooth Stones for Pastoral Work*
- Eugene Peterson and Marva Dawn, *The Unnecessary Pastor*

How We Serve Ministry Workers

Retreats

Designed for church workers and their spouses, Grace Place Wellness Retreats teach practical preventive and restorative self-care. Those who attend our retreats rediscover the joy of their vocation. We can even bring a Grace Place Retreat to your church, teaching the principles of wellness to your ministry team or congregation.

Books and Resources

Our latest book, *Reclaiming the Joy of Ministry*, along with the accompanying workbooks, teaches how to avoid the hazards of ministry life so you can have a long, joyful, and fruitful career.

Grace Place Wellness Community

Our online forum is open to pastors with a passion to learn from, encourage, and support one another in wellness practices. Our goal: To become effective ministers of the gospel of grace.

Guest Speaking and Consulting

Executive Director (and career pastor) Darrell Zimmerman creates personalized programs for district, circuit, regional, and church events. He presents conversation-based programs intended to help participants grow stronger in spiritual, emotional, and physical wellbeing.

Free Resources

You can receive our Daily Devotional or Weekly Wellness tips directly to your inbox, or you can check out all of our previous articles online. We also provide inspiration and practical advice for preventive self-care several times a week on Facebook and Instagram.

LEARN HOW TO LIVE — AND MINISTER — FROM A *PLACE* CALLED *GRACE*.
Find out how at GRACEPLACEWELLNESS.ORG

G CONFESSIONAL STATEMENT

Which theological documents or confessional statements of your denomination offer helpful insight into the Office of the Ministry? For example, Lutherans might begin with Article 14 of the Augsburg Confession and the same article in the Apology of the Augsburg Confession.

H LITURGICAL AND MUSICAL RESOURCES

During this season of meditation and preparation, which liturgical resources or music that address Vocational wellness will you utilize to enhance your times of worship and devotion?

1 INSTITUTIONAL RESOURCES

CONGREGATIONAL What gifts has God given you in the people of the congregation that might be helpful in this time of contemplation?

MINISTERIAL ASSOCIATION What peer relationships do you have with people nearby that might offer insight and encouragement as you dream for the future?

DISTRICT/SYNOD What resources are available to you through your regional judicatory or national offices?

COMMUNITY/PROFESSIONAL What other resources available in your surrounding community might be helpful?

PEOPLE RESOURCES

COACH How might a trained life coach be helpful to you in this journey? A coach will ask challenging questions along the way to help you expand the horizons of things you might consider and to help keep you accountable to the process you design.

Does your denomination or regional office offer coaching assistance or referral? Consider searching for a coach through a personal recommendation or on the International Coaching Federation's website www.coachfederation.org/find-a-coach

MENTOR How might a mentor be helpful? Who is someone of wisdom and experience that you respect and trust who has taken a similar journey and that might be a sounding board for you on your journey? How would their counsel and encouragement be helpful?

COUNSELOR Are there emotional wellness issues involved in your brokenness that would benefit from the help of a trained therapist or counselor? A counselor who can examine your situation from an outsider's perspective can often help you get "unstuck" from situations where you are so close to the issues yourself that you don't recognize patterns of behavior or influences that have contributed to your situation.

SPIRITUAL DIRECTOR Your faith walk impacts every aspect of life. A spiritual director can help you explore your practice of the spiritual disciplines and offer guidance for new dimensions of your growth in Word and Sacrament.

PEER GROUP Who else do you know in ministry that might be interested in joining you in this process of growth in Vocational wellness? Consider inviting other likeminded peers to join you in a collegial group to take this journey together.

VISION STATEMENT: MY DESIRED FUTURE CONDITION

In case you have jumped ahead to this part of the process without spending considerable time in study, meditation and prayer in the resources mentioned above, please consider pausing for a little while longer and spending a bit more time with the process. Here's why.

Many coffee drinkers enjoy their morning cup from an instantly brewed, one-cup coffee maker. Some coffee aficionados prefer the slower, but much tastier, cold brew process. Visions for the future need time to percolate, to slowly penetrate the bedrock of long-formed habits and the calluses formed by the way we've always done things until our hearts and minds begin to become infused with the fresh flavors of a new, more desirable future.

This might be a good time to reflect for just a bit longer on what Vocational wellness might look like. Frederick Buechner once gave a wonderful description of the call into ministry. For a look, do an internet search for "Frederick Buechner commencement address to Union Seminary." Where else could you look for a good narrative description of what the Vocational life of a church worker looks like?

In Lesson Ten of "Reclaiming the Joy of Ministry" we discussed "resilient" as a better metaphor for church worker health than "robust" or "strong." It's now time for you to envision a future in Vocational ministry that includes the important themes you've been considering, and may include some of the themes we've suggested: a balance of hubris and Humility; resilience under duress; the fruit of the Spirit which is Gentleness; the regular experience of joy in ministry, etc.

We recommend a lengthier, multiple page narrative description of your desired future and also, when you have completed the longer description, a brief, easily remembered summary description of your new life of Vocational wellness.

Go back to the previous Step and review the letter to a friend describing your current situation.

Now take some time to imagine that day when things have taken a turn for the better. If everything fell into place perfectly for the next six months or twelve months, if you were at your very best place Vocationally, how would you describe it?

Take some time now to write another letter to your friend from that better place.
What's happened?

What blessing from the gospel of Christ have you experienced that has given you strength and healing?

What choices have you made that helped turn things around?

Who has come alongside you?

What new behaviors have made a difference for you?

What have you learned and applied in your life that has made a difference?

𝓛 JOIN THE GRACE PLACE WELLNESS COMMUNITY

Consider once again how participating in the Grace Place Wellness Community might be of benefit to you. Join us – **www.community.graceplacewellness.org**

𝓂 SUMMARY CONCLUSION OF STEP THREE: MY VISION FOR VOCATIONAL WHOLENESS

Now use the letter to draft a one page vision statement of your desired future condition. Questions to consider as you develop this narrative description of your ideal future condition might include:

- Does this vision statement include your motivation to avoid the hurts of the past that have hindered your Vocational wellbeing?
- What difference will it make for you, for your family and for those you serve?
- How will you become more effective in ministry with these changes?
- Describe your motivation and how it is related to God's work in you and through you.
- What in your vision for the future makes it clear that it's for the sake of God's kingdom and not your personal reward?
- How does it represent your joyful obedience from a free and willing spirit?
- With whom could you discuss your vision for Vocational wellness and how will you arrange for a time to meet together?

Before Proceeding to Step Four...

THE READINESS FOR CHANGE INDEX

There comes a point in the seasons of life when the discomfort of a situation becomes so great that we realize that changes have to be made. When things got bad enough, Popeye the Sailor used to say, "I can stands what I can stands, but I can't stands no more!" The healing, replenishing power of the gospel of Christ is always, in every situation and phase of life, the right and inheritance of every Christian. When the burdens of the struggle under the cross become so heavy that the weight of them hinders our service to the Lord, it's time for retreat, to hear the gentle whisper of the Lord, as Elijah did on Mount Horeb (see 1 Kings 19).

Self-care means making adjustments. Those adjustments might mean one-time interventions, such as a conversation with church leaders, seeking the forgiveness of someone we have wronged, or taking a vacation or a sabbatical leave. The adjustment might mean a behavioral change in lifestyle, such as a change in patterns of devotional time and devotional style, new patterns of sleep and exercise, or a weekly date night.

The readiness for change index is a simple way for someone contemplating making changes to assess the likelihood of actually making and staying with a behavioral change. The index delineates five phases of readiness for change. The further along the Readiness for Change index you are currently, the greater the likelihood that you will eventually incorporate behavioral change into your daily habits. The five stages are:

- **PRE-CONTEMPLATION** A new behavior has not yet been considered, and the likelihood of making a behavioral change is very low.

- **CONTEMPLATION** A change is being considered for the first time, but the likelihood of beginning a new behavior and staying with it is still quite low, but getting closer.

- **PREPARATION** Plans for what the change might look like are formulated and evaluated. The costs connected to a new behavior are weighed against the costs of not changing.

- **ACTION** Plans for change are implemented for the first time. It can often take weeks or months, and sometimes even years to reach this stage and take action for the first time. One-time interventions are completed at this stage.

- **MAINTENANCE** In the case of ongoing life-style changes, strategies to resist the return to former patterns of behavior are designed and implemented so that the new behavior will become a regular discipline. Grace to cover lapses is central to this stage!

If you have been working the process this far, you have clearly reached the Contemplation stage. At this point, you may or may not yet be feeling like Popeye the Sailor.

Where do you see yourself on the Readiness for Change Index?

How are you feeling about the journey so far?

it's time
for retreat,
to hear
the
gentle
whisper
of the
Lord

Consider what some potential changes might be in store for you as you seek renewal and list them here. You can refer back to this list as you journey through the Preparation stage in the upcoming exercises in the process.

SHOULD I COMPLETE STEP FOUR?

The completion of "Reclaiming the Joy" through Step Three puts you at a crossroads. Before continuing, you'll need to assess whether or not to work the process outlined in Step Four, "Welcoming the Healing Spirit," before continuing with Step Five, "Welcoming the Spirit of Joy."

Step Four is designed to help you develop a plan for Restorative Wellness. In many instances, experiencing Vocational brokenness can leave someone deeply wounded. Before developing a plan to establish Sustaining Wellness practices to ensure joy in ministry for the long term (Step Five), those who have been deeply hurt must first find healing for their wounds. We serve well from our scars, but ministry is hindered by open wounds that have yet to experience Christ's healing touch. If the symptoms of brokenness you identified in Step Two still cause you significant hurt, if you find it difficult to leave the past behind, if you are still grieving or angry because of them, we recommend that you work the process outlined in Step Four, "Welcoming the Healing Spirit."

Step Five is designed to help you develop a plan for Sustaining Wellness. If your past experiences have been placed in their proper perspective, if forgiveness for wrongs committed by others has been mutually offered and received, and if your focus is already joyfully looking toward the future where you will find ways to avoid the distress you've experienced in the past, then you should move directly to Step Five, "Welcoming the Spirit of Joy."

Please remember, if you should discover that the wounds of the past have not fully healed, it may be necessary to pause and look back to seek the Lord's restorative care before proceeding forward with your design of a sustaining wellness plan.

Take a moment to reflect at this crossroads. What are the indicators that you may need to work through past hurts before continuing with your plans for the future?

What are the indicators that the Lord's grace has healed the wounds of the past, that you're ready to move forward?

Step Four
Welcoming the Healing Spirit

This Step requires considerable time for slow reflection and contemplation and should not be rushed. Make a commitment to trust the process outlined in this Step. Make a note of your starting date and also note reminders in your calendar to check your faithfulness to the process every few weeks.

Starting Date_____ Dates to assess progress_____

PRAYER FOR THE JOURNEY

How have the lessons of Step Three changed the focus of your prayer for the wellness journey? How will you remember to stay active in prayer for this next part of your discovery process? Make note of your plan for prayer here.

SELECTING PRIORITY ACTIVITIES

According to the Readiness for Change Index, establishing goals that will guide your behavior in coming days means that you have moved from the Contemplation stage to Preparation.

This Step will guide you through a simple Goal Setting and Action Plan development process to bring together what you have discovered so far. Each exercise in the process builds on the previous ones to help you design your plan, so all of the following activities are considered essential.

Drafting a Goal Statement

A REVIEW OF THE PROCESS SO FAR

It's been a while since you started working through this Workbook. Take some time to review what you've discovered about Vocational wellness so far.

STEP ONE "What is Vocational wellness?" Summarize in fifty words or less what the Bible teaches about Humility, Gentleness and Vocational wellness, based on your study in Step One.

STEP TWO "Where am I right now?" In fifty words or less, summarize your present situation. Be sure to give special attention to the wounds and hurts you have experienced.

STEP THREE "Where do I want to be?" What's the heart of your vision for the future as you defined it in Step Three? State it in fifty words or less.

BEGINNING TO PUT THE PAST BEHIND

Before you start to design your personal action plan, (the steps you will follow to seek the Lord's healing touch), write out a short summary statement of what steps, what activities, what conversations what spiritual exercises will be part of your journey of healing and restoration.

How will the Lord make his healing grace a living reality for you in the weeks ahead?

What will you need to experience in order to put the hurtful experiences of the past behind so that you can begin to move forward to your desired future?

ADVICE TO SELF

This reflection exercise will require some time for contemplation. Your initial reaction is not likely to be your full answer, so please consider a least a few days of prayerful consideration before noting your response. Imagine a scene where you, your personal self, come to you, as a church work professional, seeking advice for the situation you have outlined in Steps One through Three.

What would you typically tell your "client" (yourself) to do?

What needs repentance and confession?

How does the good news of God's love and forgiveness apply to your situation?

How would you suggest that your client fully welcome God's healing grace and love?

What key resources (scripture, books, spiritual disciplines, etc.) do you often advise others to utilize in similar situations?

After time for reflection, write out your advice to yourself. This will help give direction to the goals you will develop next.

𝒟 IDEAS FOR WELCOMING THE HEALING SPIRIT

Brainstorm eight or ten potential directions for goal statements. What can you envision yourself doing in the days ahead that will help make your desired future a reality? This is the "wild and crazy" possibilities list. Let your mind roam free; good directions are often suggested by outlandish possibilities. Be sure to include any thoughts that have come to mind as you worked through the previous Steps.

Select two or three of the best ideas and write rough drafts of goals for them.
What might it be like to go in the direction suggested by each goal?

Which would best help you achieve your desired future?

Where do you sense the Holy Spirit's leading toward his desired future for you?

Put your list in priority order, beginning with the goal that you are most willing to begin striving towards that will also open you to the Spirit's healing touch. Select the one goal from your list that seems like the best place for you to begin immediate action.

GOALS THAT REACH

If you have had good experiences setting and achieving SMART goals (Specific, Measurable, Achievable, Realistic and Timed), use the SMART goals model to assess the viability of your goal statement.

If, however, your find the SMART model a bit too technical and legalistic for your journey to wellness, evaluate your goal with the REACH model.

Is your goal statement...

R **REASONABLE** Is it the most natural next step to take as you seek substantial healing and restoration from your past hurtful experiences? Does it motivate you to take the next steps necessary? If not, write a more reasonable goal here.

E **ENJOYABLE** Can you expect to celebrate the Spirit's gift of joy along the way as you experience the healing touch of Christ? Does the goal outline activities that you will find pleasant, or even fun? If not, write a more enjoyable goal here.

A **ACHIEVABLE** Most goals we set need to be cut in half. Can you expect to see benefit from your actions soon enough to keep you moving forward? If not, write a more achievable goal here.

C **CHRIST-FOCUSED** Will your goal lead you to the gifts of grace and healing that only Jesus can give? Does it require you to welcome and receive his ministry to you through Word and Sacrament? If not, write a more Christ-focused goal here.

H **HOLY SPIRIT-LED** Is the Spirit's guidance from your earlier study (Steps 1-3) apparent in this goal? Can you confidently say, "This is where God is leading me"? If not, write a more Holy Spirit-led goal here.

𝓕 DEVELOPING AN ACTION PLAN

Write the goal to which you will begin striving here. Set a time each day for the next week to contemplate your goal.

Review the Readiness for Change Index. How ready are you to begin implementing the behavioral change that will help you to achieve your Vocational wellness goal?

> Focused on God's gracious work in us
>
> —
>
> not on our own efforts for self-improvement.

After spending a few days in contemplation of your goal statement, consider whether or not it addresses the painful experiences of the past by inviting the healing grace of Christ.

What indicates that your goal is focused on God's gracious work in you and not on your own efforts for self-improvement?

How does the achievement of your goal rely on the grace of Christ and the leading of the Spirit?

Describe here the confidence you have that this goal is God's intention for you as you make your next steps toward substantial healing for Vocational wellness.

Commit your goal statement to memory. Where else should it be written down in order to keep it before you daily?

What else will you do to keep it in the forefront of your mind and in your heart?

After Contemplation and Preparation comes the time for Action. List here the specific actions you will take in the first weeks of your wellness journey.

What will be your easily achievable and simple to do first step toward pursuing your goal?

How will your Action Plan utilize the gospel resources you identified in Step Three?

INSTITUTIONAL RESOURCES

If you did not utilize available Institutional resources in the previous step, consider if now might be the time. What resources to aid your journey might be found...

In your Congregation

In your Ministerial Association

Through your District/Synod

In your Community

How will you involve them?

H PEOPLE RESOURCES

If you have not utilized People Resources available all around you, now is the time to reconsider. Descriptions are found in Step 3 J, page 44. Which of these companions would offer you the encouragement and support you need?

_____Coach

_____Mentor

_____Counselor

_____Spiritual Director

_____Peer Group

How will you contact them?

1 ACCOUNTABILITY AND ENCOURAGEMENT

"Though one may be overpowered, two can defend themselves. A cord of three strands is not easily broken." Ecclesiastes 4:12

Who will know my goal?

How will they keep me accountable?

Why do I consider this person trustworthy enough and supportive enough to trust with this responsibility?

How will they know what kinds of affirmation and encouragement I will need along the way?

Sketch out an accountability plan that includes two or three ideas about whom you might contact, when you will, and how you will share what you need from their partnership.

JOIN THE GRACE PLACE WELLNESS COMMUNITY

Consider once again how participating in the Grace Place Wellness Community might be of benefit to you. Join us – **www.community.graceplacewellness.org**

J PRAYER JOURNALING

As you seek the Lord's healing grace in prayer, what will be your practice of keeping a written record monitoring the Spirit's sculpting/healing work in the months ahead?

K PERIODIC ASSESSMENT OF MY WELLNESS JOURNEY

Set a series of dates in your calendar a few weeks apart to review your progress toward your wellness goal. Write the dates here and in your daily calendar.

On the dates set for your goal and action plan review, ask yourself the following:

"Remembering that the goal is never perfection, am I experiencing Christ's substantial healing of hurts from the past?"

"How does Paul's example in Philippians 3:12-14 give me encouragement to press on toward the goal?"

"What adjustments do I need to make to my goal statement (see the REACH model above)?"

"What adjustments do I need to make to my timeline?"

"What adjustments do I need to make to my action plan?"

"Who could help me reflect on my journey so far?"

The wellness journey always includes stops and starts, as well as progress and setbacks along the way. Abraham, Moses, David, Peter and all the saints who have gone before us relied on God's grace and patience on their journeys.

How has God invited you to put off your old nature, be made new, and put on the new nature over the past few weeks?

How has God's love sustained you and carried you through your setbacks and frustrations so far?

L CELEBRATION OF THE LORD'S HEALING WORK

When you are ready to move forward to Step Five, take time for gratitude and praise to God for his work of healing in your life.

What will you do to celebrate God's goodness to you?

Who will celebrate with you?

How will you share with them what's been happening on your journey?

M NEXT REACH GOALS FOR CONTINUED HEALING

Return to the remaining possible goals outlined in exercise D. of Step Four. Would it be helpful to follow the same path for one or more of these potential goals as you did for your top priority? Why or why not?

SUMMARY CONCLUSION OF STEP FOUR

Write down a summary of the substantial healing you have experienced in recent days in pursuit of your goal.

Welcoming the Spirit of Joy

This Step requires considerable time for slow reflection and contemplation and should not be rushed. Make a commitment to trust the process outlined in this Step. Make a note of your starting date and also note reminders in your calendar to check your faithfulness to the process every few weeks.

Starting Date_____ Dates to assess progress_____

PRAYER FOR THE JOURNEY

How have the lessons of Step Three or Step Four changed the focus of your prayer for the wellness journey? How will you remember to stay active in prayer for this next part of your discovery process? Make note of your plan for prayer here.

SELECTING PRIORITY ACTIVITIES

According to the Readiness for Change Index, establishing goals that will guide your behavior in coming days means that you have moved from the Contemplation stage to Preparation.

This Step will guide you through a simple Goal Setting and Action Plan development process to bring together what you have discovered so far. Each step of the process builds on the previous to help you design your plan, so all of the following activities are considered essential.

Drafting a Goal Statement

REVIEW OF THE PROCESS SO FAR

If you didn't work through the process in Step Four, it's been a while since you started working through this Workbook. Take some time to review what you've discovered about Vocational wellness so far. If you completed Step Four, review your notes from this same exercise.

STEP ONE "What is Vocational wellness?" Try to summarize in fifty words or less what the Bible teaches about Humility, Gentleness and Vocational wellness, based on your study in Step One.

refreshed & renewed

STEP TWO "Where am I right now?" In fifty words or less, see if you can summarize your present situation. Be sure to give special attention to the wounds and hurts you have experienced.

STEP THREE "Where do I want to be?" What's the heart of your vision for the future as you defined it in Step Three? Try to state it in fifty words or less.

STEP FOUR "What have I learned from my past?" God reveals himself in our cross-bearing. In fifty words or less, how has he shown you his love and touched your life with substantial healing of the past?

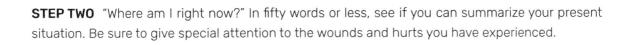

Step Five
Welcoming the Spirit of Joy

𝓑 LOOKING TO THE FUTURE

Following his mountaintop retreat in 1 Kings 19, Elijah embarked on new adventures in ministry, refreshed and renewed for the tasks at hand. Make some notes here about your Action Plan for guarding against those forces that threaten the joy of service according to your gifts in church ministry.

What are you learning about Vocational self-care?

How are you planning to apply what you've learned?

What are the Vocational pitfalls you will be learning to avoid?

What Vocational boundaries will need to be established to ensure sustained vitality in ministry?

ADVICE TO SELF

This reflection exercise will require some time for contemplation. Your initial reaction is not likely to be your full answer, so please consider a least a few days of prayerful consideration before noting your response.

Imagine a scene where you, your personal self, come to you, as a church work professional, seeking advice for the situation you have outlined in Steps One through Three.

What would you typically tell your "client" (yourself) to do?

What needs repentance and confession?

How does the good news of God's love and forgiveness apply to your situation?

How would you suggest that your client fully welcome God's sustaining grace and love as you move forward on your wellness journey?

What key resources (scripture, books, spiritual disciplines, etc.) do you often advise others to utilize in similar situations?

After time for reflection, write out your advice to yourself. This will help give direction to the goals you will develop next.

IDEAS FOR WELCOMING THE SPIRIT OF JOY

Brainstorm eight or ten potential directions for goal statements. What can you envision yourself doing in the days ahead that will help make your desired future a reality? This is the "wild and crazy" possibilities list. Let your mind roam free; good directions are often suggested by outlandish possibilities. Be sure to include any thoughts that have come to mind as you worked through the previous Steps.

Select two or three of the best ideas and write rough drafts of goals for them.
What might it be like to go in the direction suggested by each goal?

Which would best help you achieve your desired future?

Where do you sense the Holy Spirit's leading toward his desired future for you?

Put your list in priority order, beginning with the goal that you are most willing to begin striving towards that will also open you to the Spirit's leading as you move toward a healthier future. Select the one goal from your list that seems like the best place for you to begin immediate action.

 GOALS THAT REACH

If you have had good experiences setting and achieving SMART goals (Specific, Measurable, Achievable, Realistic and Timed), use the SMART goals model to assess the viability of your goal statement.

If, however, your find the SMART model a bit too technical and legalistic for your journey to wellness, evaluate your goal with the REACH model.

Is your goal statement...

 REASONABLE Is it the most natural next step to take as you seek substantial healing and restoration from your past hurtful experiences? Does it motivate you to take the next steps necessary? If not, write a more reasonable goal here.

 ENJOYABLE Can you expect to celebrate the Spirit's gift of joy along the way as you experience the healing touch of Christ? Does the goal outline activities that you will find pleasant, or even fun? If not, write a more enjoyable goal here.

 ACHIEVABLE Most goals we set need to be cut in half. Can you expect to see benefit from your actions soon enough to keep you moving forward? If not, write a more achievable goal here.

 CHRIST-FOCUSED Will your goal lead you to the gifts of grace and healing that only Jesus can give? Does it require you to welcome and receive his ministry to you through Word and Sacrament? If not, write a more Christ-focused goal here.

 HOLY SPIRIT-LED Is the Spirit's guidance from your earlier study (Steps 1-3) apparent in this goal? Can you confidently say, "This is where God is leading me"? If not, write a more Holy Spirit-led goal here.

✏ DEVELOPING AN ACTION PLAN

Write the goal to which you will begin striving here. Set a time each day for the next week to contemplate your goal.

Review the Readiness for Change Index. How ready are you to begin implementing the behavioral change that will help you to achieve your Vocational wellness goal?

After spending a few days in contemplation of your goal statement, consider whether or not it will set you a path toward the Vocational wellness you envisioned in Step Three.

What indicates that your goal is focused on God's gracious work in you and not on your own efforts for self-improvement?

How does the achievement of your goal rely on the grace of Christ and the leading of the Spirit?

Describe here the confidence you have that this goal is God's intention for you as you make your next steps toward Vocational wellness.

Commit your goal statement to memory. Where else should it be written down in order to keep it before you daily?

What else will you do to keep it in the forefront of your mind and in your heart?

After Contemplation and Preparation comes the time for Action. List here the specific actions you will take in the first weeks of your wellness journey.

What will be your easily achievable and simple to do first step toward pursuing your goal?

How will your Action Plan utilize the gospel resources you identified in Step Three?

INSTITUTIONAL RESOURCES

If you did not utilize available Institutional resources in the previous step, consider if now might be the time. What resources to aid your journey might be found...

In your Congregation

In your Ministerial Association

Through your District/Synod

In your Community

How will you involve them?

PEOPLE RESOURCES

If you have not utilized People Resources available all around you, now is the time to reconsider. Descriptions are found in Step 3 J, page 44. Which of these companions would offer you the encouragement and support you need?

_____Coach

_____Mentor

_____Counselor

_____Spiritual Director

_____Peer Group

How will you contact them?

1 ACCOUNTABILITY AND ENCOURAGEMENT

"Though one may be overpowered, two can defend themselves. A cord of three strands is not easily broken." Ecclesiastes 4:12

Who will know my goal?

How will they keep me accountable?

Why do I consider this person trustworthy enough and supportive enough to trust with this responsibility?

How will they know what kinds of affirmation and encouragement I will need along the way?

Sketch out an accountability plan that includes two or three ideas about whom you might contact, when you will, and how you will share what you need from their partnership.

JOIN THE GRACE PLACE WELLNESS COMMUNITY

Consider once again how participating in the Grace Place Wellness Community might be of benefit to you. Join us – **www.community.graceplacewellness.org**

PRAYER JOURNALING

As you seek the Lord's healing grace in prayer, what will be your practice of keeping a written record monitoring the Spirit's sculpting/healing work in the months ahead?

PERIODIC ASSESSMENT OF MY WELLNESS JOURNEY

Set a series of dates in your calendar a few weeks apart to review your progress toward your wellness goal. Write the dates here and in your daily calendar.

On the dates set for your goal and action plan review, ask yourself the following:

"Remembering that the goal is never perfection, am I experiencing Christ's guidance as I walk by faith developing new, healthier practices in ministry?"

"How does Paul's example in Philippians 3:12-14 give me encouragement to press on toward the goal?"

"What adjustments do I need to make to my goal statement (see the REACH model above)?"

"What adjustments do I need to make to my timeline?"

"What adjustments do I need to make to my action plan?"

"Who could help me reflect on my journey so far?"

The wellness journey always includes stops and starts, as well as progress and setbacks along the way. Abraham, Moses, David, Peter and all the saints who have gone before us relied on God's grace and patience on their journeys.

How has God invited you to put off your old nature, be made new, and put on the new nature over the past few weeks?

How has God's love sustained you and carried you through your setbacks and frustrations so far?

L CELEBRATION OF THE LORD'S SUSTAINING WORK

As you near completion of this phase of your wellness journey, take time for gratitude and praise to God for his work of renewal in your life.

What will you do to celebrate God's goodness to you?

Who will celebrate with you?

How will you share with them what's been happening on your journey?

M SUMMARY CONCLUSION OF STEP FIVE

How do you envision the future of your Vocational self-care for sustained joy in ministry?

Write down a summary of your intentions for the days ahead according to the Action Steps you developed. How will you keep yourself conscious day by day of your intentions?

How will you be held accountable to maintain the practices you're working on for the many years that lie ahead?

Return to the remaining possible goals outlined in exercise D. of Step Five. Would it be helpful to follow the same path for one or more of these potential goals as you did for your top priority? Why or why not?

Grace Place Wellness Ministries is committed to providing church work professionals with ongoing encouragement and wellness resources. Be sure to visit our website www.GracePlaceWellness.org to see our latest offerings.

Final Words of Encouragement

GRACE ALONG THE WAY

It's the nature of every journey of faith to experience setbacks along the way. How will you remember the practice of Baptismal renewal, to put off the old nature when you have stumbled along the way through confession and repentance, to be made new in the attitude of your mind through the grace of forgiveness, and to put on the new nature by returning to the process of reaching your goals?

Growth toward maturity in Christ is always the work of God in our lives, never our own efforts. In this life God has warned us that perfection is never the goal. By the grace of God, we seek merely substantial healing of our brokenness through the development of godly disciplines that open us to the Holy Spirit's sculpting work.

How has the Lord offered you comfort and grace along the way in your journey so far?

How will the grace of Christ bless you and cover you as you continue this imperfect journey toward wellness?

OUR PRAYER FOR YOU

And remember that your friends at Grace Place Wellness Ministries pray for you and your family as you bear the cross of ministry in the church every day. May our favorite prayer become one of yours:

"Lord God, you have called Your servants to ventures of which we cannot see the ending, by paths as yet untrodden, through perils unknown. Give us faith to go out with courage, not knowing where we go, but only that Your hand is leading us and Your love supporting us; through Jesus Christ our Lord. Amen."[i]

i Lutheran Service Book, "Collect For Guidance in our Calling," (St. Louis: Concordia Publishing House, 2006), p. 311.

Made in the USA
Monee, IL
17 February 2021